HÄGAR

THE HORRIBLE

Hagar Leads the Way

Dik Browne

ATTICA

PUBLICATIONS

Introducing . . .

HÄGAR THE HORRIBLE a hard-working Barbarian businessman. He's in sacking and looting.

His wife, HELGA. She finds civilising Hagar a 24-hour-a-day job!

This is HAMLET, their son, a real problem child! He insists on wearing his hair short, bathing, reading and otherwise behaving in a very unbarbarian manner.

HONI, their daughter, is sixteen years old, and still not married!

But that's not the end of Hagars troubles . . . there's also LUCKY EDDIE who must be the most hopeless assistant in history!

© 1987 King Features Syndicate, Inc.
First published by Attica Publications 1987.

ATTICA Publications is an imprint of Argus Communications Ltd., DLM House, Edinburgh Way, Harlow, Essex, CM20 2HL, England.

ISBN 1 85176 059 8

Printed and bound in Great Britain by Cox and Wyman Ltd., Reading.

DIK BROWNE·

GUESS WHO ?!

JUST RUNNING DOWN TO THE LOCAL STORE FOR SOME MORE HORRIBLY GOOD CARTOON BOOKS, COLOUR ALBUMS, CALENDARS, DIARIES, REMINDER CALENDARS, GREETING CARDS, GIFTWRAP AND TAGS – ALL FEATURING ME OF COURSE!
WHY NOT JOIN ME BEFORE THE BARBARIANS GET THERE!

DiK BROWNE

Hagar Books to collect:

CARTOON BOOKS   **PRICE £1.25**

Hagar Tries Again
Hagar Has A Go
Hagar In A Fix
Hagar On The Rampage
Hagar Gets It All
Hagar Leads The Way
Hagar Takes A Break

COLOUR ALBUMS   **PRICE £2.25**

Hagar Lets Himself Go
Hagar In Trouble
Hagar The Hero
Hagar Never Say Die

Prices and availability subject to change without notice.